CW00832651

SMUGGL

SMUGGLER'S GIRL

The Extraordinary Story of Margaret Catchpole

By Sally Harris

Illustrated by Edward Blake

ANGLIA *young* BOOKS

First published in 1990
by Anglia Young Books
Durhams Farmhouse, Ickleton
Saffron Walden, Essex CB10 1SR

Illustrations by Edward Blake

British Library Cataloguing in Publication Data
Harris, Sally
  Smuggler's girl: the extraordinary story of
Margaret Catchpole.
  1. New South Wales. Catchpole, Margaret
I. Title
994.40292

ISBN 1-871173-08-6

Typeset in Palatino
and printed in Great Britain by
Redwood Press Limited, Melksham, Wiltshire

CHAPTER ONE

It was summer 1789. Margaret Catchpole and her younger brother, Edward, were on their way to a christening in the village of Nacton in Suffolk. As they walked along the sandy track above the River Orwell, Edward bent to pick up a stone and flung it towards the water:

'How many christenings have we been to at the Cracknells?'

Margaret laughed: 'I've lost count.'

'This one should be fun,' said Edward. 'Some sailors are coming.' He gave Margaret a sidelong glance. She had grown into a very pretty girl, with her dark hair and flashing eyes.

'Huh!' replied Margaret, tossing her head, 'I don't want anything to do with sailors!' She gathered her long skirts and started running. 'Race you to the gate,' she yelled over her shoulder.

'Peg, you're nearly 16. You're meant to be dignified!' laughed Edward, as he overtook her.

They soon arrived at the Cracknell's cottage, and Margaret helped set out food and drink for the party after the christening.

Later, when they all came back from the church, Margaret held the new baby while the Cracknell family fussed about settling their guests. She had just handed the baby back to Mrs Cracknell when a stranger broke away from a group of men and come towards her:

'That's a lucky baby! I never had such a pretty person to look after me!'

Margaret was startled. She turned round and looked up. The man who had spoken to her had laughing blue eyes, a tanned face, and dark hair caught back in a pigtail.

Mr Cracknell paused beside them: 'This is Will Laud,

Margaret. As you can see, he's a sailor – and a rare cheeky one, too!

Will Laud didn't deny it. He folded his arms and grinned.

'And this is Margaret Catchpole, Will,' said Mr. Cracknell. Her father works with me on Denton's farm. He's the ploughman.' He paused, took a swig at his ale and then wiped his hand across his mouth. 'Peg here has a way with horses, too.' he said.

Margaret blushed. She hoped Mr. Cracknell wasn't going to tell, yet again, the story of her ride to Ipswich. It embarrassed her. But, sure enough, out it came.

'Yes, she rides as if she were born in the saddle. She was the talk of the neighbourhood a while back.'

'Why?' asked Will.

'I fetched the doctor from Ipswich, for Mrs. Denton at the farm,' muttered Margaret, looking down at the floor.

'More like she flew to fetch the doctor,' said Mr. Cracknell. 'She rode those four miles in record time as if the devil were at the horse's heels. She rode right through the town to Orwell Place, sitting astride like any plough boy. And on market day, too!'

Will grinned: 'And was the doctor in?'

Margaret raised her head: 'Yes he was. Dr Stebbing was really grateful, so was Mrs Denton.' Then Margaret looked Will Laud full in the face:

'And *they* never tease me about the ride, either,' she said.

Will raised an eyebrow. Young Margaret was obviously a girl of spirit.

Margaret busied herself with the food and drink but, in between passing and pouring, she chatted and laughed with the rest of the company, particularly with Will Laud. He teased her, but she liked him; and she noticed that her brothers liked him, too.

Later, when the other guests had gone, the Cracknells, the Catchpoles, and the Lauds sat down to drink a last pot of ale.

'Tell us where you've been, Will,' said Mrs Cracknell.

Will put down his pot and stretched: 'I've only made a few trips to Holland this year,' he said. 'I've mostly been boatbuilding with my uncle in Aldeburgh.'

Will's father nudged him: 'Tell them about Captain Bargood,' he said. Then, as Will hesitated, he continued: 'Captain Bargood thinks a lot of Will. We're hoping he might give him command of one of his ships.'

'I'm going to see him tomorrow,' said Will.

'He's got a good number of ships, hasn't he?' asked Margaret's father.

Will nodded: 'Yes, and some beauties among them'.

'And some houses around the coast,' said Mr Laud.

'He's got nothing to do with smugglers, then?' asked Mr Catchpole. 'I've heard it whispered . . . '

'Oh no. He's very respectable,' said Will.

Mrs Cracknell stood up and started to collect the ale pots: 'These days, a lot of respectable people get themselves mixed up with 'free trading' as they call it,' she said, almost to herself.

But Will had heard her: 'Yes. And it's easy to see why. If smugglers want help - a fast horse, say, or an empty barn - and people refuse, they find their horse stolen and their barn burnt to the ground.'

Mrs Catchpole nodded: 'Some folks near Bawdsey had their cottage burnt down. They reckon it was because they'd talked too much about the free traders they knew.'

'Aren't the smugglers ever caught?' asked Margaret.

'*Some* are caught,' said her father. 'I've seen them, good and dead, hanging near Sizewell. But most of them are too well organised.'

'Too many smugglers and too few customs men,' said Will.

Edward was excited: 'Do you know any smugglers,' he asked.

'No. But I can guess at a few. When I stay with my uncle in Aldeburgh, I sometimes hear muffled hooves going through the town in the middle of the night. And everyone knows that the horses are carrying silk, or spirits or tobacco.'

Edward sat on the edge of his seat, his eyes wide: 'If you see a stuffed cat in the window of Wolverstone Lodge, across the river here, they say it's a sign for the smugglers. A sign that the customs officers aren't about.'

Will jumped to his feet, suddenly restless, and soon the party broke up. The Laud family left first, but not before Will had invited himself to call on the Catchpoles. Margaret waved goodbye:

'Good luck with Captain Bargood', she called.

CHAPTER TWO

But it was some time before Will Laud was given command of a ship. During the following months, he had a few short runs down the coast, then one across to Holland. On this last trip, he had acted as captain, under the guidance of an experienced mate called John Luff. John Luff was a rough, thickset man who gave Will good advice and seemed to like him.

In between these jobs, Will Laud spent a lot of time visiting Margaret. Will was a bright, talented young man and the whole family enjoyed his company.

'She could do a lot worse than marry young Will,' said her father, after one of these visits.

Then, at last, Captain Bargood summoned Will once more. They were to meet early the next morning on Felixstowe beach.

Surely, *this* time, he'll offer me a ship, thought Will, as he hurried off to see Margaret. And, if he does, I'll no doubt have to board straight away. Will slowed down as he approached the Catchpole's cottage. He'd have to tell Margaret that she wouldn't see him again for some months if he *did* get his own ship. A captain couldn't leave his vessel every time it stopped at a nearby port.

The Catchpole family seemed to sense that this was a special visit and they left the young couple to themselves. It was no surprise to anyone when, later that afternoon, Will announced that he'd asked Margaret to marry him, and that she'd accepted.

'You said you didn't want anything to do with sailors,' said Edward.

'That was before I'd met one,' laughed Margaret.

'Promise you won't forget me if I'm away for half a year, Peg?' said Will, and there was a trace of anxiety in his voice.

'I'll tie a knot in my 'kerchief to remind me of you,' she said, smiling. Then she squeezed his hand and said quietly: 'How *could* I forget you?'

He smiled at her: 'If I'm not given a ship, I'll soon be back, but if I'm not back in three weeks, you'll know that I'm away to make our fortune.'

'Mind you come back with satins, silks and jewels then!'

Will stayed late that night and when, at last, he left, Margaret walked a little way down the track with him. Then they parted and she stood in the moonlight, her heart full to bursting, and watched until his figure merged with the shadows of the trees.

• • • • •

Will was on the beach at Felixstowe at first light the next morning. He leant against a cliff and waited nervously for Captain Bargood. A mist hung low over the water and the silence was broken only by the gentle lapping of waves on the shingle. It seemed impossible that this was the same sea which could smash ships like matchwood.

Am I really going to be the captain of a ship, he thought. It was a dream he'd had ever since he had sat in the slow creaking tub of a ferry with this father. He used to pretend that he was on one of the large sailing ships which cut through the waves at the river estuary and were soon a speck on the horizon as they made their way to some strange faraway shore.

The captain of a ship, he thought. And Margaret for a wife!

His daydream was broken by the faintest movement on the water. He started, then, peering out to sea, saw the shape of a rowing boat coming towards him through the mist.

There was no sound, not even the creak of an oar.

A sailor was rowing, and another man – a short, plump man – stood upright in the prow of the boat as if rock, not water, were beneath his feet. Even through the mist, Will could see his neat pointed beard and the cane under his arm. As the boat grounded gently on the shore, the plump man jumped over the side. He dismissed the sailor and then came straight up the beach towards Will.

Will walked down the beach to meet him. They shook hands and for a few moments there was silence. Bargood looked Will up and down, then he spoke: 'There's a ship waiting out there for you my boy.'

Will's heart leapt. He could hardly speak for excitement. 'Oh thank you sir,' he said, grasping Captain Bargood by the hand. 'I won't let you down, I promise. Shall I come with you now? I've got my bag.'

But Captain Bargood seemed in no hurry. 'All in good time, Will. All in good time. First you must hear the conditions of service.'

But Will was hardly listening. His eyes were straining through the mist, trying to get a glimpse of the ship. 'Oh, I'm sure I'll manage them,' he said.

But Captain Bargood took Will by the arm, walked him

over to a cliff ledge and motioned him to sit down. Then he talked softly and firmly and, as he spoke, Will's eager face became more and more serious. At last, Will got to his feet, and his voice was flat: 'I have always dreamed of having my own command Captain Bargood. But I'll not do this. My father does some work for the government and I'd be working against him.'

'Will, my boy,' said the Captain, smiling. 'This is quite a usual way to trade nowadays. People call it free trading.'

'It's smuggling,' whispered Will.

'But everyone has a part in it along these coasts!'

'No Captain, not everyone. And not me. I have a sweet-heart who wants me in one piece, not hanging from a gibbet or dead on the beach by the sword of a customs man.'

'If you have a girl, Will, then there's all the more reason to join us. In two years you'll have half the profits from every voyage as well as your wages – and those are three times as much as you'll ever earn from the land.'

Will shook his head: 'No.'

There was a long silence. Captain Bargood rose to his feet and looked out to sea: 'Well then, I hope your sweetheart will be happy to live her life as a servant dressed in coarse clothes.'

Will remembered Margaret's words: 'mind you come back with satins, silks and jewels.' She'd been joking, of course, but still . . .

Captain Bargood was already half way down the beach. Unsure of himself now, Will picked up his bag and started off over the shingle after him, his feet crunching on the stones. The Captain stopped without looking round.

As Will drew level with him, the mist was rolling away from the water and out there, lit by the rising sun was a ship, riding sleek and handsome on the silver morning sea.

'It's the *Alde*!' breathed Will. 'I helped build her. We named her after the river where we built her. She's a beauty!'

At that moment, the life of Will Laud was changed for ever. Common sense left him and he said, firmly: 'I'm with you, Captain!'

Captain Bargood turned then and smiled: 'I knew I was right about you, boy! Come and meet the mate and the crew and you'll be away to Holland today, to happiness and fortune, even before the sun is high.'

As Will got into the rowing boat he saw why he hadn't heard it approach. The oars and the rollocks were swathed in sailcloth to muffle the sound.

CHAPTER THREE

One evening, many weeks later, the Catchpoles had a strange visitor. He was a dark, rough looking man, dressed as a farm labourer.

He said a sailor had stopped him on the beach at Felixstowe and asked him to deliver a bundle to Margaret.

Margaret clapped her hands in excitement. It must be a present from Will! Immediately she wanted to go to Felixstowe to see Will, but the man stopped her, telling her roughly that a Captain couldn't leave his vessel. Then he was gone, hurrying away down the track.

The family gathered round while Edward opened the bundle and the contents spilled out onto the cottage floor. There was fine silk and satin, Brussels lace, kid gloves, a silver tipped pipe, a box of tea and many other things. Expensive things which no labourer could ever afford.

There was a tense silence in the little cottage as the family stared at the presents. No-one said it aloud, but they all shared the same thought.

White-faced, Margaret gathered everything up and replaced it carefully in the coarse sacking, then she took the bundle up to her bedroom, flung herself down on her mattress and sobbed as if her heart would break.

The others looked at each other fearfully. At last, Mr

Catchpole spoke: 'He was no labourer, the man who came just now. He was a sailor. A smuggler sailor. And Will Laud sent him.'

• • • • •

He was right. The 'labourer' was John Luff, Will Laud's mate, the man who had been so helpful to Will on his trial run as a captain.

That same evening, after he had delivered the presents to Margaret, John Luff was talking to Captain Bargood in the snug cabin of the *Alde*. It was anchored not far from the Catchpole's cottage, across the river at Pin Mill. They knew they were safe from an inspection by the customs men because the white stuffed cat had been sitting comfortably in the cottage window at Wolverstone.

Luff grinned: 'She's a good-looker, Will Laud's girl,' he said, taking a long sup of ale. 'And spirited, too. She was all for going to Felixstowe to find him.' He took another sup and his face hardened: 'Suspicious of me, she was, but the goods may tame her.'

His hairy features looked grim in the flickering light of the oil lantern and his lips curled to show strong tobacco-stained teeth.

Beside him, the neat figure of Captain Bargood was a complete contrast. 'You say Laud is proving a good captain?' he asked.

Luff nodded: 'Yes, he takes advice and has a real feel for the sea. He'd be a daredevil in a tight corner, too. And the crew like him.'

Captain Bargood half closed his eyes: 'Umm. It would be a pity to have him distracted by that girl and put off his er ... career. There's none of our captains living who've gone back to working on the land, eh John?'

'No, not *living*, Captain,' said John Luff, and they both laughed.

Captain Bargood yawned: 'I'll speak to him when he comes back from the tavern.'

A few minutes later, the oil lamp swung as Will came down the hatch and into the cabin. He stopped, surprised to see Captain Bargood.

'Good evening, Captain. I didn't know you were coming on board.'

'I came to congratulate you, Will. You've run in some good cargoes – nice and quietly, too.'

Will smiled, then turned to John Luff, anxious to know if his mission had been successful.

'How's Margaret? Did they like the gifts?'

John Luff looked at him slyly: 'Margaret's fine, and her family. They were really pleased with the gifts.'

'Do they suspect . . . ? Were they shocked?'

Luff shook his head.

Will squared his shoulders and turned for the door: 'I'll be off to see them now then.'

But Captain Bargood barred his way. 'Steady, lad. Not so fast. Don't go and see them just yet.'

'But I've not set foot there for over three months!'

'That's nothing. Give it twice that time. We've some good runs coming up.'

'But I'll only spend an hour, just to see her. No-one will notice me slip across at night.'

'The moon will be up and the tavern people know you're here. You can't be too careful. Besides, you should be away on the next tide.'

13

Will dropped his hands to his sides, dejected. He'd waited all these weeks to see Margaret and now . . .

Captain Bargood spoke again: 'You're doing well, boy. Keep it that way and lie low a while longer. Then, in a few years you'll have a fortune and be able to live off it in comfort without having to hide from the law.'

• • • • •

Time went on and Will certainly did have some good runs. One very exciting one, too, when a customs cutter had chased them. But the *Alde* had been too fast and Will's seamanship too good!

Now they were anchored off a bleak strip of coast called Shingle Street at the mouth of the river Ore. False rumours had been filtered through to the customs men that goods would be landed at Sizewell Gap, several miles up the coast and it seemed that, yet again, the rumours had worked. There were no warning lights from the shore. It was very peaceful, for the sea was quiet that night. Yet, for some reason, the silence was oppressive and Will was nervous. But he showed none of this to the crew, and aloud he said 'Lower away' and watched the first rowing boats pull silently for the shore with their load of contraband.

It had been agreed that Will should visit Margaret after this run. He had sent Luff with two more bundles of gifts and, each time, Luff had assured him they'd been well received. Luff didn't tell Will that he had just flung the sacks through the cottage door and then run off.

Margaret hadn't touched the gifts, but her family couldn't bring themselves to throw away such fine things and they shared them with the Cracknells. Suspicion was aroused among the neighbours, and it didn't take long for Will Laud's name to be linked with the fine clothes

14

and possessions. The customs men already knew about Will Laud.

The rowing boats returned for the last time to reload and Will, his thoughts full of Margaret, went back across with them. The muffled oars made no sound and soon the boat ground gently on the shingle. Will's heart was beating wildly. At last, after all this time, he'd be seeing Margaret again!

He could hear the horses pawing the ground, anxious to be away. There were no jingling harnesses, for these had been muffled like the oars. There would be no galloping, either, with this enormous rich load, and it would be safely stacked away before the King's men realised that they had been bluffed. Will smiled to himself. There were plenty of safe storage places nearby owned by sensible gentlemen who enjoyed good brandy in exchange for the loan of a barn or cellar!

'We'll get the beasts away now, captain,' Luff whispered.

Will was about to reply when the call of a nightjar suddenly pierced the darkness. Luff stiffened: 'That's no bird!'

Will went numb with fear. Then, he grasped his pistol and the feel of the cold metal steadied him. 'Watch out, boys,' he whispered. 'I think they've fooled us!'

As he spoke, figures rose like spectres in front of them. The King's men had been lying on the beach hidden by shingle!

Will drew his pistol. 'Go for them,' he yelled.

A tall figure, heading the group, bore down on him. Beside Will, Luff gasped: 'It's Barry!' He spat out the name.

Edward Barry! The ruthlessly clever guardian of the coasts, well known to smugglers and most feared by them.

Will Laud aimed his pistol and fired.

Barry swerved and the bullet went wide. Now, he was coming at Will, sword in hand, the blade flashing through the murk. But Will had a sword, too, and he lunged at Barry. Then suddenly, someone hit him from

behind. He fell to his knees and Barry raised his sword. Will shrieked in agony and his last conscious thought was of Margaret.

CHAPTER FOUR

Margaret couldn't sleep that night so she got up quietly, taking care not to disturb the others, and wandered outside. For some time, she leant against the cottage door, thinking of Will and worrying about him. The dawn would break soon. She yawned – and then stiffened. Faintly at first, then getting louder, came the unmistake-able sound of a horse galloping up the track to the cottage.

Could it be Will? Her heart started thumping with excite-ment and her thoughts were in turmoil. What would she say to him? She was almost certain he was a smuggler, but she knew she would find it impossible to turn him away.

Nearer and nearer came the hoofbeats and Margaret shrank against the door, half frightened, half excited, as the horse and rider came into view.

The rider pulled harshly at the reins and the horse skid-ded to a halt. A rough voice – a voice she recognised – called out to her: 'Will's wounded. Come quickly.'

It was that man again. The man who had brought the gifts!

Sick with disappointment that it wasn't Will, it took Margaret a moment to take in what the man was saying. Then he leant down from the horse and shook her arm: 'Hurry woman, for God's sake! Will Laud is dying!'

Margaret felt numb. Desperately she tried to collect her thoughts: 'All right, I'll come at once. Wait there while I get my cloak.' She stumbled into the cottage, rammed on her boots and flung her cloak round her shoulders. Then she snatched some homemade healing ointments from the corner cupboard and called into the family's sleeping quarters: 'Will's wounded. I must go to him!'

Then, before anyone could stir themselves to stop her, she dashed outside again. The man pulled her up behind him and, in the pale light of dawn, they set off on a nightmare journey to find Will.

It was terribly uncomfortable, but Margaret hardly felt the bumping and jolting. She could only think of Will. 'What happened?' she gasped, holding tightly to the man's waist. 'Where is Will?'

'A fight with the coastguards,' shouted the man, riding hard and looking ahead. 'He's been cut by a sword and he was left for dead. I got away, then came back and found him. I took him off the beach and carried him to a cottage near Felixstowe.'

'What's your name?'

'John Luff. I'm Will Laud's mate.'

John Luff! Even in her misery, Margaret realised what that name meant. John Luff was notorious on this coast as a smuggler. It had been John Luff, then, who had brought the first bundle of gifts to her, disguised as a labourer, and no doubt it was John Luff who had brought the others, too, and slipped away before anyone saw him.

At last the sea came into view and Margaret saw a small building outlined against the morning sky. Luff reined in the horse and jumped off. Margaret ignored his out-stretched hand, and got off by herself, then she pushed past him and went into the cottage.

She stared about her. There was just one room and the only light came from the open door. In the middle of the dirt floor was a table and in the far corner there was a poor bed on which lay a motionless figure covered by sacking. In an instant, Margaret was at the bedside.

Gently, she removed the sacking which covered Will's face. Then she gasped and shrank back against the wall, her hand over her mouth.

Half of Will Laud's face had been cut away!

John Luff hovered in the doorway: 'Is he still alive?'

Trembling, Margaret forced herself back to the bed and flung off the sacking. She pulled up Will's shirt and laid her ear to his bare chest.

He was warm and his heart was beating!

'Yes,' she whispered. Then she looked helplessly round the dirty hovel. She must overcome her fear of the wound and find some clean cloth to bathe and bind Will's face. Seeing nothing suitable, she tore strips from her own clothes.

She turned to Luff: 'Tell me where to get clean water, then leave me alone with him.' When he'd shown her, she wiped away the blood from the raw flesh and bathed Will's face, then she smeared the herbal ointments onto the strips of cloth and gently bound them round his head.

Luff watched her in silence then, with a gruff promise to see that she got some food, he left to go and tell Captain Bargood that they'd lost a rich cargo – and possibly their best young captain.

Once he'd gone, Margaret knelt beside the bed, her head

on the sacking. She held Will's hand, closed her eyes and prayed.

· • • • • •

For two days and nights Margaret hardly slept. Often Will called out, delirious with fever. Usually Margaret couldn't understand what he said, but sometimes she heard her name.

John Luff came once or twice with food, but he never stayed long. He was uneasy in Margaret's presence and she made no secret that she distrusted him and held him at least partly responsible for enticing Will into smuggling.

Then, on the third night, Will felt cooler. His temperature had gone down and, for the first time, he was aware of Margaret's presence. When Luff came the next morning, he noticed the change immediately: 'Captain Bargood will be pleased,' he said.

The fatigue and worry had taken their toll on Margaret and, at Luff's words, she flew into a rage: 'You and the Captain have done enough harm already,' she yelled. 'I swear that Will Laud will only work for Bargood over my dead body!'

For a moment, Margaret thought that Luff would hit her. He lunged towards her, then stopped, and a sly look crossed his face: 'Over your dead body, eh? Or maybe over yours *and* his? Think about it my lovely!'

Luff strode out of the cottage. Margaret shivered and drew her dirty crumpled cloak about her shoulders, but she was not shivering from cold. She bent over the bed to look at the sleeping Will. She was frightened for him. She realised now that it might be very difficult for him to stop smuggling, even if he wanted to. She knew that Luff was threatening her and she was scared.

Every day, Will grew stronger. He started to eat and regain his strength and he and Margaret became very close. He promised he'd give up smuggling for her and, for the time being, she said nothing about Luff's threat.

Will asked her if she'd liked her gifts: 'John Luff said you were pleased with the gifts and that you weren't shocked.'

'Then he lied,' said Margaret softly. 'Those gifts of yours have brought nothing but trouble. People gossip, Will, and it didn't take long for your name to be linked to the Catchpoles and the Cracknells. Why, even my poor father may lose his job because of you!'

'What!'

Margaret nodded: 'The gossip reached the ears of the Squire. He sent for my father and told him he'd not have anyone working on his land who deals with smugglers.'

Will hung his head: 'What a fool I've been, Peg! I'm sorry.' Then he told her the full story, about how Captain Bargood had persuaded him and how he'd dreamed of her in silks and satins. Margaret listened and her heart went out to him. At last, exhausted, Will lay back on the bed. For a while there was silence between them. Margaret was lost in thought and Will fingered the dressing on his injured face. Then, suddenly, he said: 'Will you let me look at my face now, Peg? I want to know the worst.'

Margaret started nervously. 'No, Will, not yet. It's still so raw. Wait a while longer.'

But he insisted, and started to unwind the dressing. Miserably, Margaret fetched the crude glass she'd found for herself and held it in front of him.

For a moment he just stared, then he whispered: 'I've only got half a face! Peg, why didn't you tell me? Oh God, Oh God!'

'It'll heal over, Will, I promise.' Margaret was near to tears.

Suddenly, Will yelled: 'Curse that Edward Barry! He struck me when I was on the ground. Why didn't he pierce me through the heart and be done with it! I'm no good to you like this, Peg!'

Margaret bit her lip: 'I love you, Will. I don't mind about your face.'

'But how can you love this – this half man, Peg? Why, my own father wouldn't recognise me now!'

Margaret stared at him. She had begun to see a faint glimmer of hope. 'No,' she said slowly, 'No more he would.'

Will looked at her strangely: 'What are you thinking Peg?'

'I'm thinking that maybe, after all, Edward Barry did you a favour!'

'What!'

'Yes,' she said slowly. 'After all, you were left for dead on that beach, weren't you?'

'I don't remember anything after Barry came at me.'

'You were left for dead and no doubt, when they came to fetch you, they reckoned the tide had washed you away. As far as most of the world is concerned, Will Laud is dead!'

Will suddenly realised what she meant, and from that moment they began to lay some careful plans. Will grew stronger and his face started to heal into a livid scar. At last he was well enough to leave his bed and sometimes they walked outside together though, more often, Margaret walked alone while Will rested.

• • • • •

One day, as Margaret was coming back from a solitary walk, she saw, coming out of the cottage, a short plump man with a stick and a pointed beard. He glanced in her directon, then made his way quickly down the path towards Felixstowe.

Margaret hurried back to the cottage: 'Was that Captain Bargood?' she asked breathlessly. 'What did he want? Why did he come here?'

'To see if I was better,' said Will.

'Did you tell him our plans?'

Will nodded.

'And what did he say?'

'He understood. He hardly recognised me himself. He's agreed to let me leave his service.'

'Are you *sure*, Will?' Margaret could hardly believe their luck.

Will smiled: 'Quite sure! He said that everyone thinks I'm dead and that Edward Barry's boasting that he killed William Laud, the Captain of the *Alde*! So, very soon, I'll be able to walk into the world as an honest man – a man that no-one will recognise as William Laud. I'll sign up on a Dutch ship and be home to marry you in six months!'

If Margaret had not been so excited, she would have noticed that Will's eyes did not meet hers when he told her what Captain Bargood had said.

CHAPTER FIVE

Will had lied to Margaret. Captain Bargood had *not* agreed to their plan but, instead, had offered Will a lot more money.

Will couldn't resist, and, as soon as he was strong enough, he returned to the smugglers' base on Bawdsey beach. Here, even members of his crew failed to recognise him at first! So, Will Laud changed his name to Captain Hudson and continued to smuggle while Margaret thought he'd gone to sign up on a Dutch ship, as an honest sailor.

Meanwhile, Margaret had gone to work as cook-housekeeper at Alnesbourne Priory Farm. The farm was in a beautiful position overlooking the river opposite Pin Mill and just five minutes walk from the sandy beaches which covered the mud flats at the water's edge. Every day she looked down the river and imagined Will out on the open sea or anchored safely in Harwich harbour.

Margaret enjoyed her work and did it well. The household staff and farm workers knew that her fiancé had been Captain Laud, the smuggler killed by Edward Barry, but they were mostly kind and friendly. A few, though, said that Mrs Wake, the farmer's wife, shouldn't have employed Margaret.

One day, when Mrs Wake and Margaret were in the kitchen, serving lunch to the farmworkers, one of the young men (one Margaret had not seen before) raised his glass and smiled at her: 'Your food's so good, I could eat forever!'

Margaret could see he was no ordinary farmworker and later she asked Mrs Wake who he was.

'Oh he's my husband's assistant. He's learning how to manage a farm.'

'What's his name?'

'John Barry.'

Mrs Wake was busying herself with the dishes and she didn't see Margaret start and the blood drain from her face. Barry! Was he anything to do with Edward Barry who had wounded Will?

Then Mrs Wake turned round: 'Oh I'm sorry, my dear,' she said, putting her arm round Margaret's shoulders. 'I should have known that name would upset you.'

'Is he related to Edward Barry?' whispered Margaret.

Mrs Wake nodded: 'His brother.'

'And he knows who I am?'

Mrs Wake nodded again, then she said: 'Don't worry Margaret. John Barry's a gentle young man. He'll not make trouble for you.'

And Mrs Wake was right. John Barry was especially kind and helpful to Margaret over the months that followed and, all that time, Margaret kept her secret – the secret that Will Laud was still alive.

But sometimes even she wondered whether he really *was* alive. She'd had only one brief message to say that Will had joined a Dutch ship. As time went by, Margaret became more and more disheartened.

One day she was standing out in the yard by the pump, her thoughts far away, when Mrs Wake called out: 'Margaret, we can't make the stew without any water! Stop day dreaming!'

'Sorry!' Margaret jerked back to reality and started to work the pump vigorously up and down.

The house parlour maid went by to take some linen off the line.

'Are you dreaming that another smuggler may come up the river with silks and satins!'

'If you had a sweeter tongue, you might find that some-one wanted to come up out of the sea for you,' replied Margaret crossly as she lifted the drinking water bucket and started to carry it to the kitchen.

'Well said!' laughed John Barry, coming up behind her. He took the bucket and they went back together. 'Margaret,' he said suddenly, 'Come for a walk with me after lunch. It's your afternoon off, isn't it?'

Margaret smiled: 'No, I'm sorry John. I'm visiting home today. My mother's not too well.'

'Are you staying overnight?'

'No, I'll be back by evening.'

•••••

The sun had nearly set when Margaret approached Priory Farm. She came over the crest of the high ground above the river and started to walk across the last field. Then she stopped in surprise. Sitting on the stile at the far corner of the field was John Barry. He waved and smiled as she came closer and, even before she reached him she knew, in her heart, that he was going to ask her to marry him. And she knew, too, that she could never say yes to him.

As the sun sank below the hill, they sat and talked. He did, indeed, ask her to marry him and, as gently as she could, she refused him, explaining that she still loved Will Laud.

'But Margaret, he's dead. My brother killed him! Can't you ever forget him.'

Margaret looked at John. He was gentle and honest and

she was fond of him. Could she trust him with her secret? It would be such a relief to share it.

She took a deep breath, then, looking him full in the face, she said: 'If I tell you something John, will you swear never to reveal it to another living soul?'

John frowned: 'Yes. Yes, of course.'

Margaret looked up at the sky. She got to her feet: 'It's almost dark. I'll tell you as we walk back to the house.'

So Margaret told him everything. How she had nursed Will back to health and how Will had mended his ways and was now an honest sailor on a Dutch ship, unrecognisable as the old Will Laud.

For a long time, John said nothing. Then, at last, he sighed: 'I don't think Will Laud will ever settle down and make you happy, Margaret.'

'I have to hope, John,' she whispered. 'I love him.'

CHAPTER SIX

Three months had gone by and now it was harvest time on the farm. Margaret was busy in the kitchen when a figure appeared in the doorway.

'Can I have a drink of water, miss?' said a deep foreign voice.

She turned, and was not particularly surprised to see a sailor standing there. Ships sometimes anchored in the creek below the farm and, in hot weather, sailors often stopped to ask for a drink on their way to Ipswich.

She put down the saucepan she was holding and gave him some water. He drank it quickly, then wiped his hand across his mouth: 'Does Margaret Catchpole work here?'

Margaret looked at him suspiciously: 'Why?'

'I have a message for her.'

Margaret's heart leapt. Could it be a message from Will at last? She looked fearfully round the kitchen, but there was no-one about. They were all helping to get in the last of the harvest.

'I'm Margaret Catchpole,' she said quietly.

The sailor looked at her keenly, then said: 'I'm from a . . . er . . . Dutch ship and my captain says you call him Will.'

Margaret was too excited to notice the hesitation in his voice. She nodded: 'Yes, go on' and while she waited to hear more, the whole world seemed to stop.

'He says he will wait for you here tomorrow night down by the creek.'

At *last*! He'd come at last! And she'd see him tomorrow!

'When? What time?' she managed to stutter.

'Nine o'clock.'

Margaret smiled. Her heart was so full she thought she might cry. She turned away from the sailor: 'Tell him I'll be there!'

• • • • •

The next day was a busy one for Margaret. She had to prepare for the harvest home, a great feast which would start in the afternoon after the last load of barley had been brought into the farmyard with singing, laughter and cheering. Everyone from the farm would be at the harvest home. It was always a great celebration.

Margaret worked feverishly, serving food and drink and, all the while, watching the time. At last, she was able to slip away unnoticed.

She put on her cloak and hurried down the footpath to the creek. She stared about her. Nothing moved. There was complete silence. After a while her excitement started to drain away and she felt anxious. Would Will let her down?

Then she heard it – the gentle sound of oars – and she saw a rowing boat appear from beneath the overhanging trees at the edge of the creek. There were two people in the boat, and one of them leapt out even before it was beached.

Will!

Margaret rushed to meet him and he swung her round in his arms. She was laughing and crying at the same time and, before she could catch her breath, she heard him say: 'I've come to get you, Peg! Come away with me now and we'll be married on my ship.'

Still in his arms, she said, laughing: 'But Will, we can be married in church with my family around us.'

Will set her down gently: 'I can't do that Peg. I should be hanged as a smuggler.'

'You *won't*, Will. Everyone thinks you are dead.'

'No, Peg,' he said. 'I can't live ashore yet.'

Margaret stared at him in disbelief. Surely he hadn't forgotten their plans?

There was a laugh from the rowing boat: 'He can't live ashore because he's a free trader!'

Margaret spun round to look at the figure in the boat and, even in the twilight, she recognised John Luff. Before she could speak, Luff said, mockingly: 'Meet Captain Hudson, the notorious smuggler!'

'Quiet man!' said Will, but it was too late.

Margaret clutched Will's arm: '*You*! You're *Hudson*!' She had heard terrible stories about Captain Hudson.

Margaret was stunned. Suddenly she knew she had to get away and be alone to think. She shook free from Will, swept up her skirts and started back up the bank. But she had hardly gone any distance before powerful arms grabbed her from behind and John Luff swung her over his shoulder.

'I've got your prize Will!' he shouted. 'Back to the boat. She'll soon come round.'

Then Margaret screamed.

• • • • •

John Barry was on his way home from the harvest celebrations when he heard the scream. He stopped and listened. Then it came again, from down by the creek. He ran down the slope towards the river and, to his horror, saw Margaret struggling to free herself from two men who were trying to haul her into a rowing boat.

He grabbed a piece of wood and rushed at them: 'Leave her alone!'

Luff looked up. The voice sounded vaguely familiar and so was the face. Could it be Edward Barry!

'John,' screamed Margaret, 'Help me!'

'It's Barry's brother,' shouted Luff. He thrust Margaret away, and, in a fury of revenge, he and Will set upon John.

Margaret ran to get help but John Barry couldn't hold out against the two men. He managed to break free and started to run, but Luff raised his pistol and shot him in the shoulder. John fell and, as he tried to get up he was shot again, this time by Will Laud.

Then suddenly there were voices and they saw figures running down the bank. Margaret had raised the alarm.

Will Laud and John Luff waited no longer. They tumbled into the rowing boat and drew silently away from the shore.

CHAPTER SEVEN

For many days, John Barry lay at the farm, badly injured and weakened by fever. But at last he recovered enough to be taken home where he was nursed back to health by his mother.

Margaret left the farm, too. Everyone knew that she had been the cause of the fight on the river shore and now she was treated with suspicion.

But it was not just the change of atmosphere that made her leave. As she had feared, her father had lost his job on Denton's farm. Also, her mother was ill again and Margaret felt she must go home to nurse her and help look after the rest of the family.

One evening, just before Christmas, John Barry came to the Catchpole's cottage. He was thin, but he looked well. Margaret jumped up to greet him: 'John! How good to see you. I'm so sorry about . . . '

John Barry sat down beside her and took her hand. Before she could say anything else, he cut in: 'No more apologies Margaret. You've said them over and over again.' 'Now,' he went on, smiling, 'I've come to tell you my plans.'

And then John explained that he was going to buy some land in one of the colonies – van Diemen's Land (Australia). 'The government is selling land cheap because they want it farmed,' he said.

'But it's so far away,' whispered Margaret.

John looked at her: 'I would change all my plans if you would marry me,' he said quietly.

Slowly Margaret shook her head: 'You know I can't.'

• • • • •

So John Barry left for his new life in Australia, but just before he went, he came to say goodbye to Margaret and gave her a present – a bible.

'I'll never forget you, Margaret.'

Margaret watched him go and then, with a heavy heart, she went indoors and placed the bible in a wooden chest with her other treasured possessions.

• • • • •

A few weeks later, Margaret's mother died. It seemed then as though all those who loved Margaret had gone out of her life. She'd heard nothing from Will, her beloved mother had gone, and John Barry was thousands of miles away. She was miserable and lonely.

Margaret decided to look for another job – this time in a town – so, a few days later, she got a lift to Ipswich in a neighbour's cart. As they jogged down Bishop's Hill overlooking the docks, she remembered her frantic ride for the doctor all that time ago. She had felt at one with the horse, powerful and in command. People had stood aside for them as they had swept through the streets on their urgent errand. And Dr Stebbing had been kind to her. She would go and visit him and ask him to help her find work.

• • • • •

Dr Stebbing remembered Margaret and it wasn't long before he had obtained an interview for her with Mrs

Cobbold. The Cobbolds owned the local brewery and had a very large family.

Immediately Margaret met Elizabeth Cobbold, she felt sure she would be happy in her house.

'Dr Stebbing says you are an experienced cook,' said Mrs Cobbold.

Margaret curtsied: 'Yes Ma'am.'

'And would you be willing to help in the nursery, too?'

'Yes Ma'am,' said Margaret again.

'We are a large household,' went on Mrs Cobbold. My cook needs help with the dinner in the morning and my nursemaid needs some relief in the afternoon. We have one baby, six young children and seven older ones.' Then, seeing Margaret's astonished face, Mrs Cobbold laughed: 'My husband has been married before. I am his second wife.'

Margaret blushed and smiled nervously.

'Come and start tomorrow, Margaret. I'm sure the children will like you.'

'Thank you, Ma'am.'

Mrs Cobbold was about to dismiss Margaret, when she said: 'You look like a quick, intelligent girl. Can you read or write?'

Margaret blushed again: 'No Ma'am,' she whispered.

'Would you like to learn?'

'Oh yes, Ma'am!'

'Then, when your duties allow, you can join in the children's lessons. I shall speak to their governess.'

And so Margaret began several busy happy years with

the Cobbold family. The children adored her and the cook was delighted to have such efficient help.

One day, she and the children were walking on the shore opposite the brewery. They were near Freston Tower, a curious tall red brick building set in quiet parkland. Some workmen were carrying out repairs on it and the children were exploring. Two of the older boys had their ears to a rat's hole near the tower: 'Margaret, we can hear the rat gnawing!' they called.

Margaret, with the six young children, came to listen, too. Suddenly she shouted: 'Quick, run, all of you! Down the bank! Get away from here!'

Her voice was so urgent that they all obeyed – and only just in time. A pile of bricks from the top of the tower fell on the very spot where the boys had been. Margaret had recognised the noise. It was not the sound of a rat – it was the sound of settling masonry.

When they heard what Margaret had done, the Cobbold family were very grateful and they valued her even more highly.

As time went on, Margaret learned to read and write and she would often study the bible that John had given her.

She stopped working in the kitchen and became the head nursemaid. Then later, the family moved to a larger house on the outskirts of Ipswich, at St. Margaret's Green. Shortly after the move, the cook became ill and Margaret was asked to fill in as cook for a while. She did it well and was so popular with the household staff that she agreed to do the job permanently, for a salary that would have seemed like a fortune when she first started work at the Cobbold's.

So, the years passed. Margaret heard a rumour that Will Laud had been press-ganged into the navy to help fight the French. The navy were short of able-bodied men, and 'press gangs' were employed to force men to join. If this was really true, and Will *had* been press-ganged, Margaret knew that he might get a free pardon. But it was, after all, only a rumour and she tried to put it to the back of her mind.

And then she heard some definite news of Will Laud. News that unsettled her again and upset the calm and happy routine of her life.

CHAPTER EIGHT

On 1st June 1794, news reached England that Admiral Lord Howe had won a great victory at sea against the French. Everyone was talking about it in Ipswich and it was then that Margaret heard news of Will.

One of the gardeners came to the kitchen door: 'I was at the tavern last night, Margaret.'

'Oh yes,' said Margaret, not bothering to stop what she was doing.

'I heard news of Will Laud.'

She spun round, and her face drained of colour: 'What! Where is he? What's happened?' She felt quite faint and she had to clutch onto the edge of the table for support.

'Steady lass,' said the gardener, 'he's all right.'

Margaret sat down: 'Please tell me,' she said quietly, so the gardener continued: 'I met a sailor in the tavern. He's been sent home, wounded, but he told me he'd served in the same ship as your Will. By all accounts Will's been fighting bravely and won himself a fair bit of prize money too.'

Margaret had heard about prize money. Large sums of money were given by the government to victorious naval captains who, in turn, gave some of it to crew members who had fought well.

Margaret could hardly take it in. It was true, then. Will really *was* in the navy!

For the rest of the day, she could think of nothing but Will; were their dreams going to come true at last? Could they soon be together for ever? She hardly dared hope. That night she went to the tavern herself to meet the wounded sailor and find out everything she could about Will.

'Yes, lass,' he said. 'It's all true. I fought alongside your Will. And he sent a message for you, too.'

'What message?'

'He said to tell you that he'll come back and marry you just as soon as he gets his discharge.'

• • • • •

In the weeks that followed, Margaret found it almost impossible to concentrate on her work. Whenever she could, she visited the tavern to see if the sailors there had any more news of Will. They never did, but they all liked Margaret and they started to visit her in the Cobbold's kitchen where she would give them food and drink and listen to their stories.

However, the other servants were soon fed up with the sailors. Some of them were rude and dishonest and things started to go missing from the kitchen.

Mrs Cobbold heard about this and sent for Margaret: 'I know you are anxious to see Will Laud, Margaret. That's only natural. But you must be patient. Some sailors and soldiers are not released as soon as they hope.'

Margaret stared dully at the carpet, and Mrs Cobbold continued:

'I don't want you to allow any more sailors into the house, Margaret. They are coming on false pretences and spoiling the happy atmosphere in my kitchen.'

'Yes, Ma'am,' said Margaret, and returned to the kitchen depressed and upset.

• • • • •

The waiting was affecting Margaret. She spent more and more time at the tavern and gave less and less attention to her job. She was often sullen and preoccupied, desperately anxious about Will. Even more anxious, now, because she had heard another rumour – and it was a rumour she believed.

It was said that John Luff had sworn to kill Will Laud if Will ever returned to Suffolk. John Luff had never reformed and he looked on Will as a traitor. A traitor who had deserted smuggling to serve king and country.

Margaret was certain that John Luff meant what he said, and she was frightened.

Then, one evening, when Margaret was at the tavern, a sailor called John Cook drew her to one side. Margaret knew John Cook, but she had never particularly liked him. He had visited her in the Cobbold's kitchen and she suspected he may have stolen things from there.

'I have a message from Will Laud,' he whispered.

Margaret gripped his arm. 'What is it? Quick, tell me!'

She did not notice the sly smile that played round John Cook's mouth.

'Will is at the Dog and Bone tavern in Lambeth. He wants you to meet him there. You're to leave tonight!'

'Lambeth?' gasped Margaret. 'All the way to London. But I can't get there tonight. I'll take the mail coach in the morning.'

John Cook shook his head: 'If you take the mail coach, they'll trace you to him. Remember, John Luff has spies everywhere.'

Margaret looked at him, helplessly: 'But then, how? How can I get to Will?'

John Cook moved even closer and whispered: 'I hear you ride well?'

Margaret nodded.

'Then, get yourself dressed up as a stable boy and I'll meet you at the Cobbold's stables at 11 o'clock tonight.'

'But what . . . ?'

'Shh!' said Cook. 'I'll find you a horse. Just trust me. And not a word to a soul. You don't want John Luff finding out, do you?'

• • • • •

For the rest of the evening, Margaret was conscious of nothing except that soon she would see Will again. At 11 o'clock, she was hiding by the stables, dressed as a stable boy, waiting for Cook. She was expecting to hear the sound of hooves, but instead, Cook emerged alone from the shadows behind her.

'Where's the horse?' she whispered urgently.

John Cook smiled in the darkness: 'Right here!'

'What do you mean?'

'We'll borrow one of the Cobbold's horses,' he said.

'I can't do that!' said Margaret, horrified, 'They'd never agree!'

'You can explain later,' said Cook. 'When you've got to Will.'

Margaret hesitated, her loyalties torn: 'I'll leave them a note,' she said at last.

'No,' said Cook sharply. 'No note. Remember John Luff. You can't be too careful.'

At that moment, a soft whinny came from the stables, and Margaret made her decision. 'All right,' she said, suddenly full of resolve, 'I'll take Crop.'

John Cook watched as Margaret saddled up the strawberry roan carriage horse, muffled its hooves with sacking and led it out into the lane. He held Crop's head as Margaret swung herself into the saddle, then he made his final suggestion: 'You must sell the horse when you get to London,' he said.

'Margaret stared down at him: 'Sell him! What do you mean? I'm just borrowing him!'

'Look lass,' said Cook, suddenly fierce. 'Once daylight comes, you'll soon be noticed with a horse like that. No-one will believe your 'borrowing' story. Sell the horse as soon as you reach London, before you get to Lambeth. That way, they won't trace you to Will.'

'But I *can't*,' gasped Margaret. 'He's not mine to sell!'

'Look,' said Cook, persuasively, 'Go to the Bull tavern in Aldgate. It's nearer – this side of the Thames. Sell the horse there and leave the money for me to collect. I'll make sure Mr Cobbold gets it. Then you can make your way to Lambeth.'

'But, I can't . . . '

'Of course you can! Tell the ostler at the Bull that your master wants 100 guineas for this fine horse. He'll soon find you a willing customer.'

Margaret hesitated.

'You want to see Will Laud, don't you?' said Cook.

'Yes.'

'Then do as I say.'

'And you promise you'll give the money to Mr Cobbold?'

'I promise,' said Cook, grinning to himself in the darkness.

At that moment, Cook's idea seemed reasonable to Margaret and she didn't realise that he was playing a cruel trick on her. She was so desperate to see Will that she would have believed almost anything.

Cook let go of the bridle and Margaret set off.

Cook watched her disappear into the night. Gleefully, he rubbed his hands together. He had no idea where Will Laud was. He certainly wasn't at the Dog and Bone in Lambeth! But by the time Margaret found that out, Cook would have disappeared. Disappeared with 100 guineas in his pocket!

CHAPTER NINE

At first Margaret rode cautiously. The moon was bright and she could easily make out the old earth ramparts of the town. As soon as she was past these and in the open country, she removed the sacking from Crop's hooves and urged him on. He gathered his muscles and stretched out his neck, delighted to be free from the carriage harness.

Margaret, too, was exhilerated: 'No highwayman could catch us now,' she whispered to Crop as they galloped over the springy turf. Much later, when had just passed Colchester, Margaret heard the horn of the night mail coach from London, heading back to Ipswich. In her lighthearted mood, she was tempted to wave to it, but stopped herself just in time.

Shortly after this, she reached the village of Marks Tey. Dawn was breaking and she knew she must give Crop some food and a rest. With thumping heart, she rode up to the village inn. Would they question her business? Would they realise that she was a woman? But the ostler merely asked what she wanted and left her to attend to Crop herself. Afterwards, she went into the saloon and bought herself some ale and cheese for breakfast.

The barmaid was scrubbing the long wooden tables: 'Your master gets you to work early,' she said, but she hardly looked at Margaret.

They stopped once more for food and rest and, after that, they had to travel quite slowly as the road became busy with people making their way to London – some were in carriages, some on horseback, some pushing handcarts, and some driving sheep and geese to market.

It was early evening when at last, 19 hours after leaving Ipswich, Margaret and Crop arrived in the yard of The Bull at Aldgate. Margaret made some enquiries about selling Crop and the ostler promised to send for a dealer in the morning. So Margaret bought herself some food from the tavern then lay down in the straw beside Crop and fell into an exhausted sleep.

It was mid-morning before the dealer arrived. Margaret felt sick with nerves at the delay, but she mounted Crop and rode him round the yard. The dealer ran an expert hand down the horse's legs, then told Margaret to dismount and take off the saddle. Margaret did as she was told. She was watching the dealer so intently that she didn't notice a groom enter the yard with a piece of paper in his hand.

'I'll give you 60 guineas for him,' said the dealer, firmly.

'My master won't take less than 100 guineas,' replied Margaret, even more firmly.

Behind them, the groom handed the paper to the ostler. He looked at it, then looked at Crop. They whispered together, then the groom hurried away.

While Margaret was putting the saddle on again, the ostler drew the dealer on one side and said something to him. He nodded, but his expression never changed. Casually, he said: 'Did you ride all the way from Ipswich?'

'Yes,' said Margaret thoughtlessly.

'And your master's name . . . ?'

'John Cobbold Esquire.'

At that moment, the groom reappeared with a constable and suddenly, all eyes were on Margaret. She tried to keep calm, but her heart was pounding. Why were they staring at her like that?

The constable stepped forward: 'I arrest you for the theft of this horse,' he said.

'But I'm selling it for Mr Cobbold,' stuttered Margaret. Her eyes were wide with fright now and her hands clammy with sweat.

Then the constable held up the piece of paper and, with a sinking heart, she read what it said. It was a notice offering 20 guineas reward for Mr Cobbold's stolen strawberry roan carriage horse.

Margaret stared. How could they have found her so quickly?

The constable answered her unspoken question. 'The guard of the mail coach saw you. He recognised the horse and warned Mr Cobbold.'

Then everything started to swim before her eyes. The colour drained from her face and she felt herself losing consciousness. She fell in a dead faint at Crop's feet.

The constable bent down to loosen her clothes and remove her cap.

'Dear God!' he said, looking up at the others. 'It's a woman!'

The groom and the ostler gathered round to stare at the crumpled figure on the ground.

'They hang horse thieves,' said the groom in awe.

• • • • •

But Margaret didn't hang. At first, she was sent to the dreadful Newgate Prison in London. Mrs Cobbold visited her there and Margaret told her all about John Cook's story, but, of course, he was never traced. Nor was Will Laud.

Then, in July 1797, Margaret was moved to Ipswich jail and, shortly afterwards, she was tried at the assizes in Bury St Edmunds. She was sentenced to death, but two days later, she heard that she had been granted a reprieve. The Cobbolds had spoken up on her behalf and, instead of being hanged, she was to be transported to Australia for seven years. However, so many people were being sent to Australia for life sentences that there wasn't enough room on the ships so it was quite likely that Margaret would never actually go to Australia but spend the seven years in Ipswich jail.

Given back life and hope, Margaret determined to help the jailer and his wife. She worked hard at washing and cleaning and tried to comfort the other women prisoners. She became a trusted inmate.

• • • • •

One day, when she had been in prison for two years, Margaret was moving a clothes airer from an outside passage and, as she did so, she caught sight of a man peering at her over the wall from the debtors prison. With trembling hands, she put the airer down and rearranged the clothes. She must have been mistaken. It couldn't be him!

'Margaret? Margaret, is that you?'

This time she looked carefully. It *was* him! It was Will!

For a moment she could only stare, then she whispered: 'Will! What are you doing here?'

'I got into debt, but I'll be free soon.'

'I have another five years in here,' said Margaret, bitterly. Then she went on: 'Oh Will! Why didn't you come home to me?'

'I couldn't, Peg. I had to lie low. Bargood and Luff were trying to kill me. But they're both dead now, Peg.'

Footsteps were approaching.

'Peg,' said Will urgently, 'I have an idea. I'll tell you. Be here this time next week.'

The footsteps were getting closer and they both moved quickly away from the wall.

The following week they spoke again: 'I'll be out in a few days, Peg. And you could be out next month, too!'

'What!'

'Listen, Peg. I've thought it all out. I know a way you can escape.'

Will explained his plan, then he said: 'Please, Peg. Please do as I say. I can arrange for a boat to take us to Holland and this time we really can be married.'

Margaret hesitated, then Will said, softly: 'Five years is a long time, Peg. Please!'

She sighed. Despite all the trouble he had caused her, she knew she would agree. She couldn't stop loving Will Laud and she felt she could never be truly happy without him. And, he was right, five years was a long time.

'All right,' she said. 'I'll do it.'

CHAPTER TEN

On March 25th 1800, the governor of the jail was away. He had taken some prisoners for trial at Bury St Edmunds. One of those prisoners had been in the cell next to Margaret's. So, for the time being, that cell was empty.

After supper, Margaret fetched a bundle of clothes – sailor's clothes – which she had made secretly while helping with the prison mending. Then, her heart pounding, she hid in the empty cell.

Soon she heard the guard start his rounds: 'Are you there?' he called to each prisoner, before locking them in.

The calls came closer:

'Are you there Margaret?'

Margaret was shaking with fear. She put her mouth against the wall. She knew that her reply was muffled, but she prayed that the guard wouldn't notice.

'Yes, I'm here.'

'You sound tired.'

Please don't start talking to me, thought Margaret. Not tonight!

'Umm' she replied, through the wall.

'I'll say goodnight then.'

He turned the key in the lock of her own cell next door but then, to her horror, he walked into the empty cell where she was hiding, and stood staring out of the barred window. Margaret kept rigidly still and prayed that she wouldn't sneeze, or even breathe too loudly.

Please go, she thought. And please don't lock the door behind you!

At last he turned and walked slowly out of the cell,

leaving the door wide open. Margaret almost cried with relief. Then she settled down to wait.

Two hours later, when she heard the clock strike eleven, she tied the bundle of clothes over her shoulder and tiptoed through the silent building.

The next uncertainty was the outside door into the yard. Would it be locked? She had no way of knowing. Looking nervously round, she approached it. Her hand closed over the handle and her heart stood still as she pushed it down.

It swung open and Margaret walked through into the yard. For the first time, she allowed herself to smile.

Earlier in the week, she had noticed a a flower trellis in the corner of the yard. She fetched it and leant it firmly against the wall where a spike on top was broken. She climbed up the trellis and, with the help of a clothes prop, managed to fix a rope washing line round the spikes. She shinned up this rope, then leant on the bar where the spike was broken while she drew up the rope and let it down the other side of the wall. Next, she grasped the top of the rope and turned head over heels as the spikes revolved with her. She was over! She recovered her breath and climbed down to freedom – and to Will!!.

'Peg!'

He was there! And for the moment, nothing else mattered.

'Quickly, Peg. Change into the sailor's clothes, then we'll go to Sudbourn, to my sister's house.'

As they hurried along the road, Margaret whispered: 'Have you got a boat?'

Will nodded into the darkness. 'We'll hide with my sister for a couple of days, then I can borrow a boat to cross the

River Ore. Another boat will meet us there and take us to a cutter and away to Holland!'

'Can't we go sooner?'

'The cutter won't be there any sooner, Peg. It's the best I could do.'

So, for the next two days, they hid with Will's sister and brother-in-law. Will's brother-in-law was a shepherd and took the sheep to graze on Sudbourn Heath. His sister was busy about the house and garden.

On the third morning she had an errand in the village but she'd not been gone long before she came running back to the cottage. She was out of breath and her eyes were round with worry: 'There's a reward out for you, Peg!' she gasped. 'Notices have been sent all over the country. They're looking for two sailors!'

Margaret's hand flew to her mouth: 'Two sailors!' she said. 'But how could they know? Unless we were seen on the road.'

'Perhaps someone at the prison saw you making the clothes,' suggested Will's sister.'

Margaret turned to Will. 'What shall we do, Will? They'll be looking for us everywhere.'

Will put his arms round Margaret. He was thinking fast: 'Find Margaret a smock,' he said to his sister. 'She must go up to the heath and help with the sheep. No-one will look for her there.'

Margaret clung to Will: 'But what about you, Will? I don't want to leave you!'

'Don't worry about me. It's you they're after this time, not me. I'll join you at dusk and we'll go straight to the boat. Be brave, Peg. We'll be all right, I promise!'

Up on the heath, Margaret thought dusk would never come. But at last Will joined her and together they hurried down to the river. Will rowed them across and then they walked to the far side of the shingle strip where the waves crashed onto the stones at their feet. As darkness fell, the moon rose and shed a pale light on the sea.

'We shouldn't have long to wait,' said Will, squeezing Margaret's arm.

Margaret clung to him. Surely, nothing could go wrong now?

'Look, Will!' she said suddenly, pointing out to sea. 'I can see a light on the horizon. Is that the cutter?'

'I expect so. It's coming landward and making good speed. They'll put a boat out soon.'

Will held Margaret tightly as they waited for a boat to be lowered from the cutter and make its way towards them.

Soon – very soon – they would be free. Margaret felt tears of joy come to her eyes.

'MARGARET CATCHPOLE!'

The voice of the prison governor exploded across the bare stones behind them.

'Oh no!' cried Margaret in anguish.

The boat from the cutter was nearly ashore. Desperately, Margaret dashed into the sea, but a wave picked her up and threw her back, senseless, onto the shingle.

The man rowing the boat saw the figures on the beach and hesitated. Then he realised that the coastguards were there and he turned the boat back to the cutter as quickly as he could.

In the moonlight, Will Laud stood over Margaret's sodden form, a pistol in each hand, and faced the law alone. The prison governor was there with a constable and a small body of coastguards headed by Edward Barry.

'Let us go,' shouted Will. 'We're not smuggling. We're just leaving the country.'

'It's Margaret we want, not you,' replied the governor.

'If anyone tries to touch her, I'll fire,' yelled Laud.

'Give her up Will Laud. She's under sentence of transportation.' It was Edward Barry shouting this time. He went on: 'We won't hurt her, and you shall go free. If I have to take her by force ... '

But before he'd finished speaking, Will fired. His shot went wide, but Edward Barry's returning shot did not. The bullet found its target and Will Laud fell dead across Margaret's senseless body.

AUTHOR'S NOTE

The Facts...

Escape from prison was a capital offence and Margaret was sentenced to death. However, once again, her sentence was changed to transportation for life.

Even at this grim time in her life, Margaret retained her dignity, sustained by the continuing friendship of Elizabeth Cobbold.

In May 1801 Margaret was sent to Portsmouth to wait in one of the old ships – prison hulks as they were called – until she boarded the *Nile*, the convict ship which took her to Australia.

Margaret endured many privations, in prison, on board the hulk, and on the *Nile*, but she always conducted herself well and this did not go unnoticed.

When she reached Australia she was immediately taken in as a cook by the Commissary-General of New South Wales. Later, she worked at a girls' orphanage and then she went to work as housekeeper to a widower and his young family who lived about 40 miles inland from the modern Sydney. Eventually, she was given 20 acres of land to cultivate in that area.

During her early years in Australia, she wrote some letters to Elizabeth Cobbold and sent her a stuffed lyre bird which was on display in Ipswich Museum in the 1920s!

Australian research finds that she continued to live quietly on her land and became valued in the district as a herbalist, a nurse and a midwife. She died on 14th May 1814, still unmarried, and is probably buried near her home, at Richmond parish church, in New South Wales.

. . . and the Fiction

The exciting story of Margaret Catchpole was made famous by Richard Cobbold, Rector of Wortham, in his book *The History of Margaret Catchpole, A Suffolk Girl*, which was first published in 1845.

Richard Cobbold was one of the many children of Elizabeth and John Cobbold, for whom Margaret worked. The events in Richard Cobbold's book are a wonderful mixture of fact and fiction.

In *Smuggler's Girl* I have followed the thread of the story which he wove and so I will finish, too, with his version of the end of the story.

According to Richard Cobbold, John Barry had been living in Australia ever since he left Suffolk. He had become a wealthy corn grower and lived, unmarried, in a mansion on the banks of the River Hawkesbury. It was a long time before he heard that Margaret was also in Australia but, when he did, he obtained a free pardon for her. They were married and had one son and two daughters.

Richard Cobbold says that John Barry died in 1827 and that Margaret moved to Sydney and lived there quietly for another 14 years.

Even though Richard Cobbold's ending to the story is not supported by fact, it is a happy ending and it would be good to believe that it might be true!

Sally Harris

PLACES TO VISIT

Cat House
Walk from Pin Mill to Wolverstone Marina where the stuffed cat can still be seen in the window of the recently restored 'Cat House'.

Alnesbourne Priory Farm
This is now a country club. The owner is happy to welcome visitors, but first please telephone Ipswich (0473) 726373

The Tolly Cobbold Brewery
This stopped production in 1989 but it can still be seen, with the house beside it (where Margaret worked) at Ipswich Eastern dock. It will soon re-open as a working museum.

Freston Tower
A footpath walk, starting opposite Freston Boot public house, leads down past Freston Tower to a very attractive foreshore.

Christchurch Mansion, Ipswich
An oil painting of Margaret Catchpole can be seen in Christchurch Mansion, which is now a museum.

Ipswich Record Office
The Record Office has accounts from *The Times* and from *The Ipswich Journal* of Margaret's ride to London, her trial and her escape.

Elizabeth Cobbold's Grave
This can be seen in St Mary le Tower church in Ipswich.